BATMAN
THE BRAVE AND THE BOLD

Raintree

Raintree is an imprint of Capstone Global Library Limited, a company incorporated in England and Wales having its registered office at 7 Pilgrim Street, London, EC4V 6LB – Registered company number: 6695582

www.raintreepublishers.co.uk
myorders@raintreepublishers.co.uk

First published by Stone Arch Books © 2013
First published in the United Kingdom in 2014
The moral rights of the proprietor have been asserted

Originally published by DC Comics in the U.S. in single magazine form as Batman: The Brave and the Bold #5.

Ashley C. Andersen Zantop Publisher
Michael Dahl Editorial Director
Donald Lemke & Sean Tulien Editors
Heather Kindseth Creative Director
Hilary Wacholz Designer
Kathy McColley Production Specialist

DC COMICS
Rachel Gluckstern & Michael Siglain Original U.S. Editors
Harvey Richards U.S. Assistant Editor

ISBN 978 1 406 26649 8
17 16 15 14 13
10 9 8 7 6 5 4 3 2 1

Printed and bound in China by Leo Paper Products Ltd

British Library Cataloguing in Publication Data
A full catalogue record for this book is available from the British Library

BATMAN
THE BRAVE AND THE BOLD®

THE CASE OF THE FRACTURED FAIRY TALE

J. TORRES.......................................WRITER
CARLO BARBERI ....PENCILLER
TERRY BEATTY....................................INKER
HEROIC AGE..............................COLOURIST
SAL CIPRIANO .... LETTERER
SCOTT JERALDS ....COVER ARTIST

GIVE IT UP! I HAVE YOUR "KEY BLASTER" AND I'VE PUT THIS WHOLE PLACE ON LOCK DOWN...
...THERE'S NO ESCAPE FOR YOU THIS TIME!
THAT'S WHAT YOU THINK, BATMAN!
I AM THE KEY.

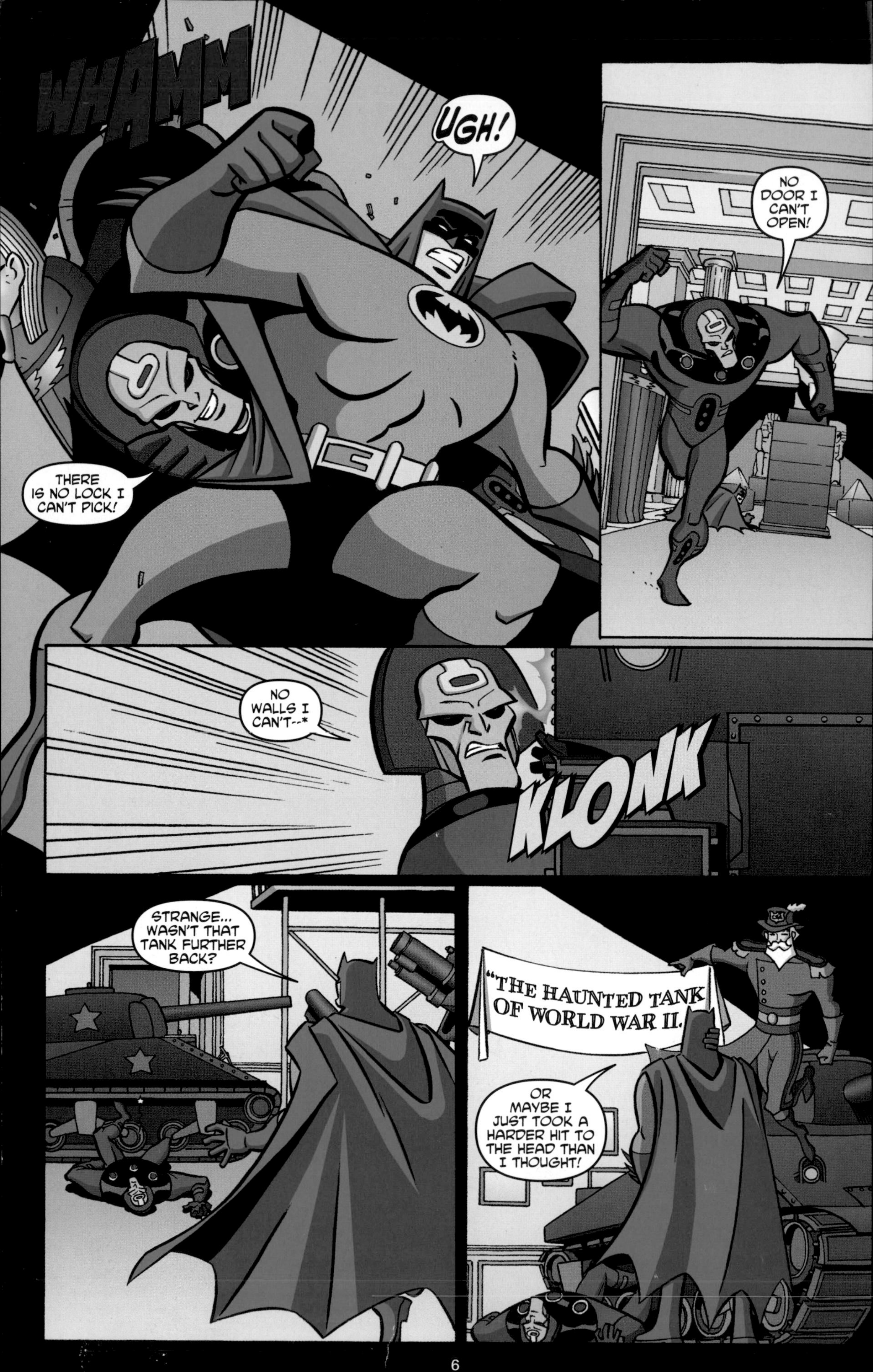
WHAMM
UGH!
THERE IS NO LOCK I CAN'T PICK!
NO DOOR I CAN'T OPEN!
NO WALLS I CAN'T--*
KLONK
STRANGE... WASN'T THAT TANK FURTHER BACK?
"THE HAUNTED TANK OF WORLD WAR II."
OR MAYBE I JUST TOOK A HARDER HIT TO THE HEAD THAN I THOUGHT!

...ANOTHER DOZEN CHILDREN HAVE GONE MISSING SINCE THE "ENCHANTED FOREST" APPEARED OUT OF NOWHERE AND TOOK OVER THE PARK! SIGHTINGS OF UNICORNS, FAIRIES, AND TALKING ANIMALS HAVE BAFFLED AUTHORITIES...
...BUT HAVE NO FEAR, FOLKS! AND REMEMBER, YOU HEARD IT HERE FIRST FROM ME, BILLY BATSON, BOY REPORTER FOR STATION *WHIZ*...

"...BATMAN IS ALREADY ON THE CASE!"
HOLD IT RIGHT THERE...
...SILLY RABBIT!
NO, NO, NO, I CAN'T STOP! OH, DEAR, I'M LATE! I'M LATE! I'M LATE!
YES, I KNOW, "FOR A VERY IMPORTANT DATE."
THE QUESTION IS: WITH WHOM? WHO'S BEHIND ALL OF THIS... MAGIC?

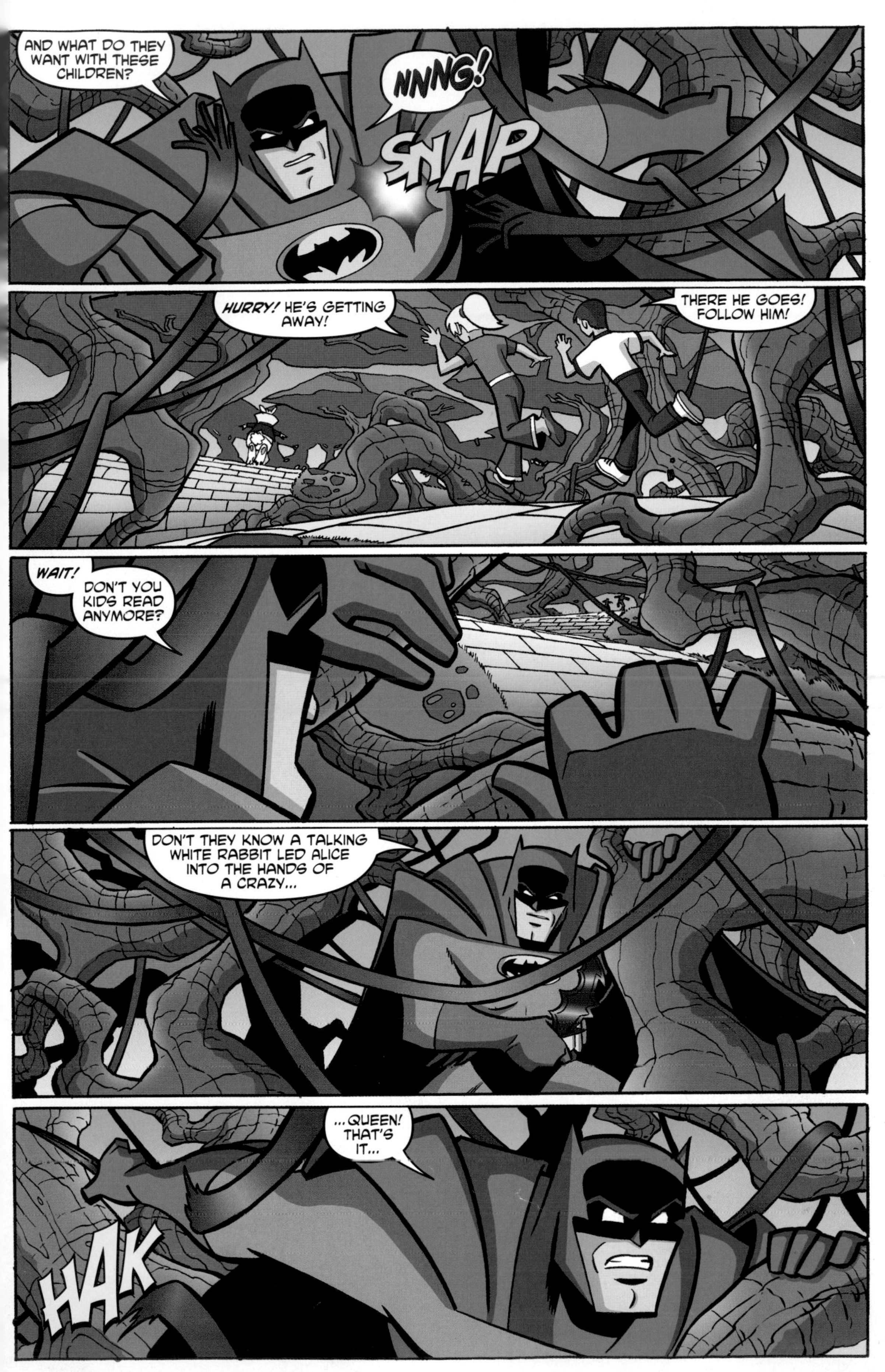
AND WHAT DO THEY WANT WITH THESE CHILDREN?
NNNG!
SNAP
HURRY! HE'S GETTING AWAY!
THERE HE GOES! FOLLOW HIM!
WAIT!
DON'T YOU KIDS READ ANYMORE?
DON'T THEY KNOW A TALKING WHITE RABBIT LED ALICE INTO THE HANDS OF A CRAZY...
...QUEEN! THAT'S IT...
HAK

"...THAT'S WHO MUST BE BEHIND ALL OF THIS!
"THE QUEEN OF FABLES."
MIRROR, MIRROR, FROM *MY* BOOK...
...TELL ME, HOW DO I LOOK?
NOT BAD FOR A 150 YEAR OLD SORCERESS! BUT YOU MIGHT WANT TO CONSIDER STEPPING UP "PRODUCTION" IF YOU KNOW WHAT I MEAN...
I *KNOW*! LOOK AT MY *HANDS*--THE MAGIC IS WEARING OFF!
THAT *PIED PIPER* MISLED ME ABOUT THE NUMBER OF CHILDREN HE COULD LURE HERE... AND THAT *WHITE RABBIT* IS ALWAYS LATE...
I NEED SOMEONE WHO CAN BRING ME *MORE* CHILDREN *MORE* QUICKLY...
...AND *THERE'S* THE ANSWER TO MY DILEMMA!
COME, MY PRETTIES, COME OUT OF THAT BOOK AND INTO THIS WORLD! BRING ME LOTS OF TEARY, WEEPY LITTLE BOYS AND GIRLS!

A DARK TOWER...OF COURSE. THIS IS WHERE ALL THE FAIRY TALE CHARACTERS ARE LEADING THE CHILDREN.
THE QUESTION NOW IS *WHY?*
WAIT... SOMETHING'S COMING OUT OF THAT WINDOW!
GOLLY, LADIES AND GENTLEMEN!
JUST WHEN YOU THOUGHT WE'D SEEN IT ALL, HERE COME...
...THE FLYING MONKEYS!
WHOA!

YOU AIRBORNE APES MAY HAVE CUT OFF BILLY BATSON'S BROADCAST, BUT NOW...
SHAZAM!
KRAKOOM
THIS IS THE CAPTAIN SPEAKING.
CAPTAIN MARVEL.

EEP?
C'MERE, BONZO...
PLEASE FASTEN YOUR SEATBELTS! WE'LL BE LANDING VERY SHORTLY!
WHOOSH
ONE DOWN, SO THAT LEAVES--
PAK PAK
HOLY MOLEY!

CAPTAIN MARVEL! DOWN HERE!
BATMAN! AM I GLAD TO SEE YOU! WE DON'T HAVE TIME TO WASTE...
...THOSE SINISTER SIMIANS ARE TAKING THE CHILDREN INTO THAT TOWER!
I KNOW, BUT WAIT! THERE'S A--
WHOOOMP
THERE'S A FORCE FIELD AROUND THE TOWER. WE CAN'T GET IN. I'VE ALREADY TRIED.
THAT... THAT FELT LIKE MAGIC...

EXCELLENT WORK. SHOW OUR NEW GUESTS INTO THEIR "ROOMS."
NOW, LET'S SEE HOW YOUR WORK IS COMING ALONG...
MMM... THERE'S NOTHING LIKE THE TEARS OF A CHILD TO QUENCH YOUR THIRST FOR... ETERNAL YOUTH!
WHAT?! IS THAT ALL? I NEED MORE! MORE TEARS!
YOU BRATS BETTER START PRODUCING MORE TEARS OR I'LL REALLY GIVE YOU SOMETHING TO CRY ABOUT!

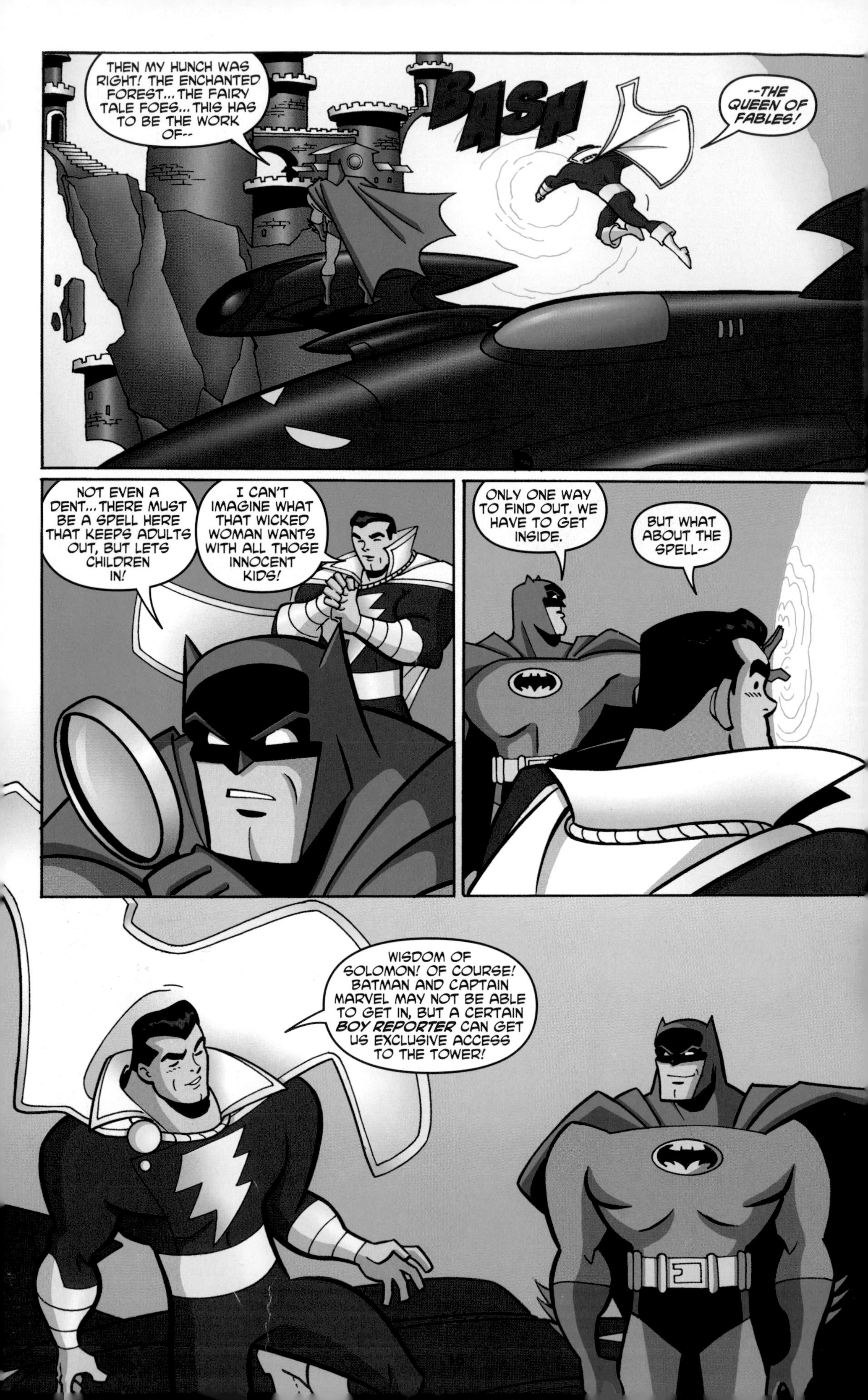
THEN MY HUNCH WAS RIGHT! THE ENCHANTED FOREST... THE FAIRY TALE FOES... THIS HAS TO BE THE WORK OF--
BASH
--THE QUEEN OF FABLES!
NOT EVEN A DENT... THERE MUST BE A SPELL HERE THAT KEEPS ADULTS OUT, BUT LETS CHILDREN IN!
I CAN'T IMAGINE WHAT THAT WICKED WOMAN WANTS WITH ALL THOSE INNOCENT KIDS!
ONLY ONE WAY TO FIND OUT. WE HAVE TO GET INSIDE.
BUT WHAT ABOUT THE SPELL--
WISDOM OF SOLOMON! OF COURSE! BATMAN AND CAPTAIN MARVEL MAY NOT BE ABLE TO GET IN, BUT A CERTAIN *BOY REPORTER* CAN GET US EXCLUSIVE ACCESS TO THE TOWER!

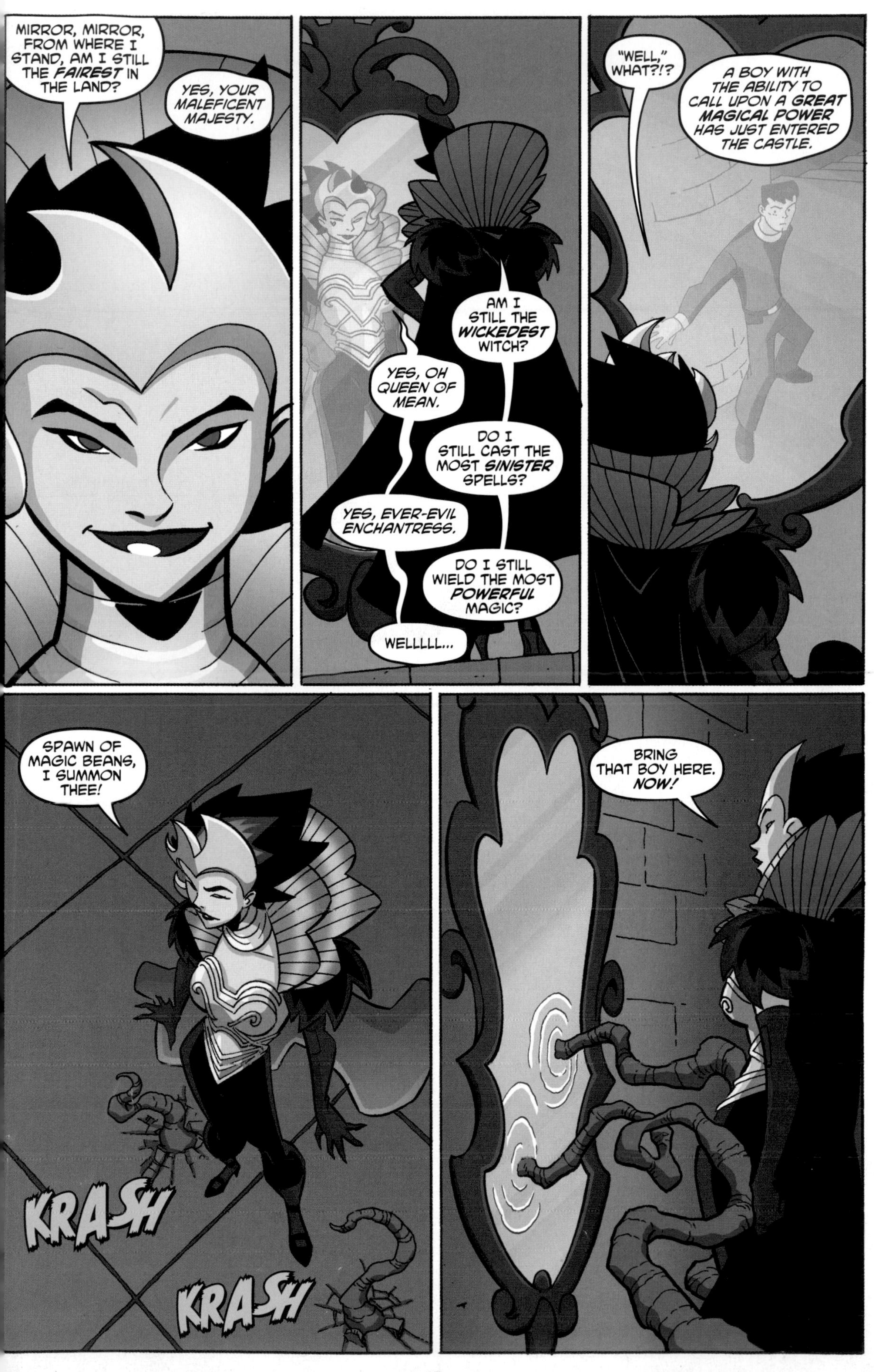
MIRROR, MIRROR, FROM WHERE I STAND, AM I STILL THE *FAIREST* IN THE LAND?
YES, YOUR MALEFICENT MAJESTY.
AM I STILL THE ***WICKEDEST*** WITCH?
YES, OH QUEEN OF MEAN.
DO I STILL CAST THE MOST ***SINISTER*** SPELLS?
YES, EVER-EVIL ENCHANTRESS.
DO I STILL WIELD THE MOST ***POWERFUL*** MAGIC?
WELLLLL...
"WELL," WHAT?!?
A BOY WITH THE ABILITY TO CALL UPON A ***GREAT MAGICAL POWER*** *HAS JUST ENTERED THE CASTLE.*
SPAWN OF MAGIC BEANS, I SUMMON THEE!
KRASH
KRASH
BRING THAT BOY HERE. ***NOW!***

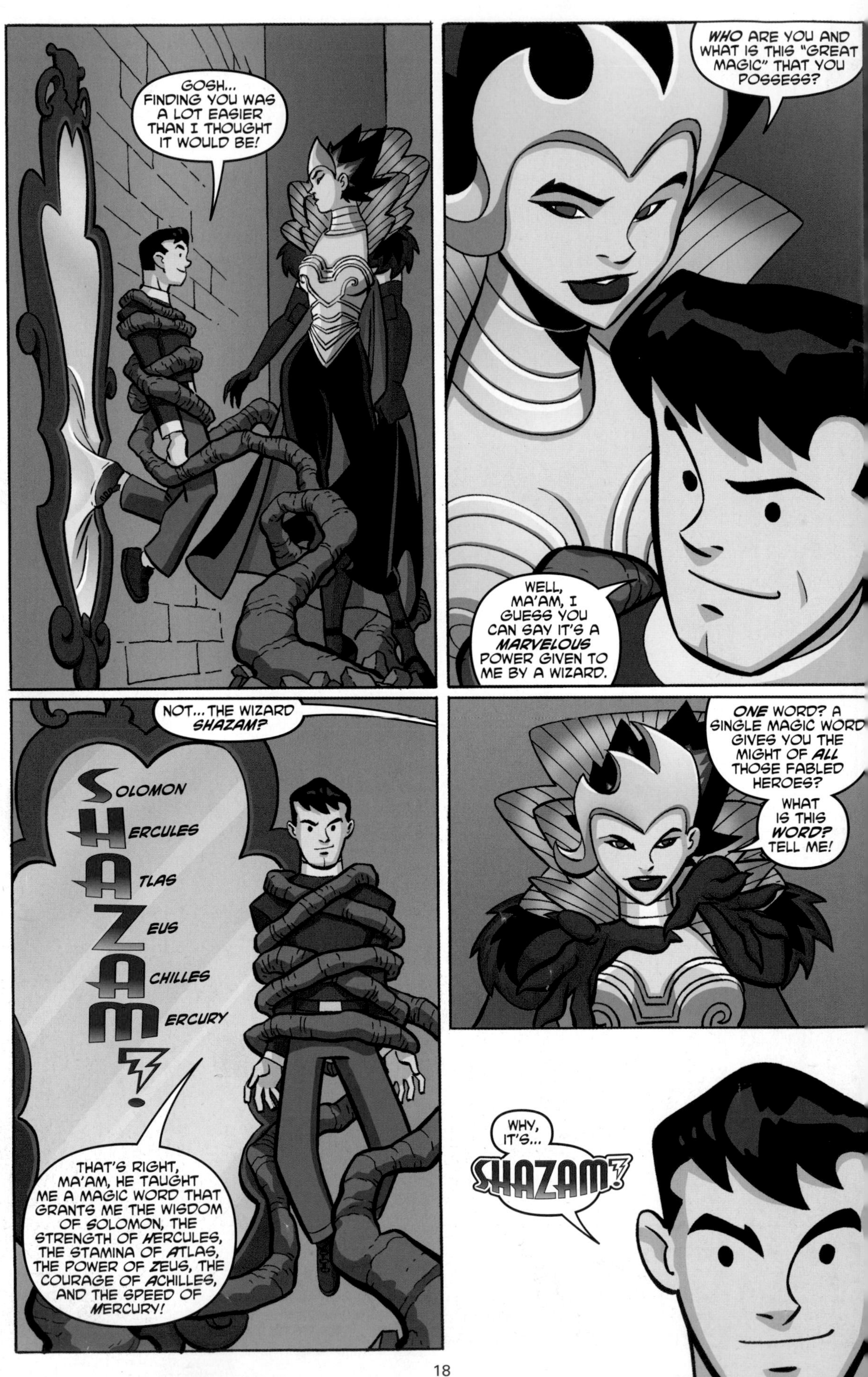
GOSH... FINDING YOU WAS A LOT EASIER THAN I THOUGHT IT WOULD BE!
WHO ARE YOU AND WHAT IS THIS "GREAT MAGIC" THAT YOU POSSESS?
WELL, MA'AM, I GUESS YOU CAN SAY IT'S A MARVELOUS POWER GIVEN TO ME BY A WIZARD.
NOT... THE WIZARD SHAZAM?
SOLOMON
HERCULES
ATLAS
ZEUS
ACHILLES
MERCURY
SHAZAM!
THAT'S RIGHT, MA'AM, HE TAUGHT ME A MAGIC WORD THAT GRANTS ME THE WISDOM OF SOLOMON, THE STRENGTH OF HERCULES, THE STAMINA OF ATLAS, THE POWER OF ZEUS, THE COURAGE OF ACHILLES, AND THE SPEED OF MERCURY!
ONE WORD? A SINGLE MAGIC WORD GIVES YOU THE MIGHT OF ALL THOSE FABLED HEROES?
WHAT IS THIS WORD? TELL ME!
WHY, IT'S...
SHAZAM!

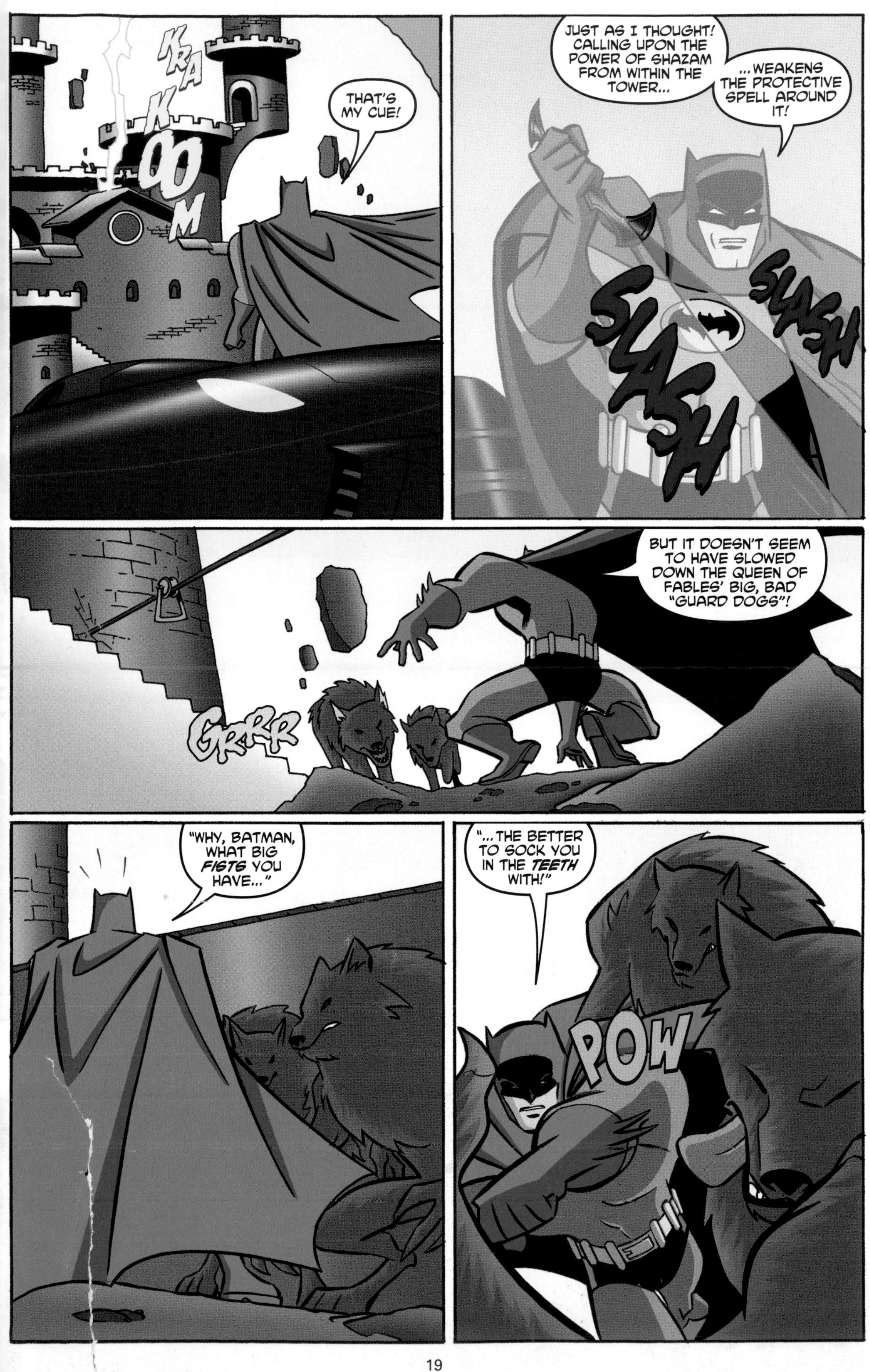
KRAKOOM
THAT'S MY CUE!
JUST AS I THOUGHT! CALLING UPON THE POWER OF SHAZAM FROM WITHIN THE TOWER...
...WEAKENS THE PROTECTIVE SPELL AROUND IT!
SLASH
SLASH
SLASH
BUT IT DOESN'T SEEM TO HAVE SLOWED DOWN THE QUEEN OF FABLES' BIG, BAD "GUARD DOGS"!
GRRR
"WHY, BATMAN, WHAT BIG FISTS YOU HAVE..."
"...THE BETTER TO SOCK YOU IN THE TEETH WITH!"
POW

MAKE THIS EASY ON YOURSELF, MA'AM! I'M GIVING YOU A CHANCE TO SURRENDER WITHOUT A FIGHT!
KRRRIIP
MWA-HA-HA-HA! DO YOU REALLY BELIEVE I WOULD DO SUCH A THING?
I BELIEVE IN GIVING PEOPLE THE BENEFIT OF THE DOUBT! I BELIEVE THEY CAN CHANGE! JUST LIKE IN FAIRY TALES!
RRIIPP
THEN WE ARE NOT SO DIFFERENT AFTER ALL...
...BECAUSE I TOO BELIEVE IN THE POWER OF TRANSFORMATION!
ARRGHH!
SHOOM

GRRAAAHHH!
CAPTAIN MARVEL... IS THAT YOU?!
KOOM
ANOTHER INTRUDER! DRAGON! GET HIM!
THAT BOOK! IT'S THE SOURCE OF THE QUEEN'S MAGIC!

HE'S *CHARGING* AT THE DRAGON! HA! THERE'S A FINE LINE BETWEEN BRAVERY AND MADNESS!
BUT THERE'S *ALWAYS* A METHOD TO MY MADNESS!
MY BOOK! GIVE THAT BACK!
I'M AGAINST BOOK BURNING, BUT IN THIS CASE...
KOOMM

NOOOOO!
I'M MELTING!
MELTIIIING--*
WHEW! I'M CHANGING BACK!
WITH THE BOOK DESTROYED, THE QUEEN IS POWERLESS, SO EVERYTHING'S GOING BACK TO NORMAL...
AND ONCE WE GET ALL THESE CHILDREN HOME, WE CAN CALL THIS CASE CLOSED, END OF STORY, THEN WE ALL GET TO LIVE...
PLEASE DON'T SAY IT.
...HAPPILY EVER AFTER.
CAPTAIN MARVEL, NOW I KNOW WHY THEY CALL YOU THE "BIG RED CHEESE."
THE END

QUEEN OF FABLES

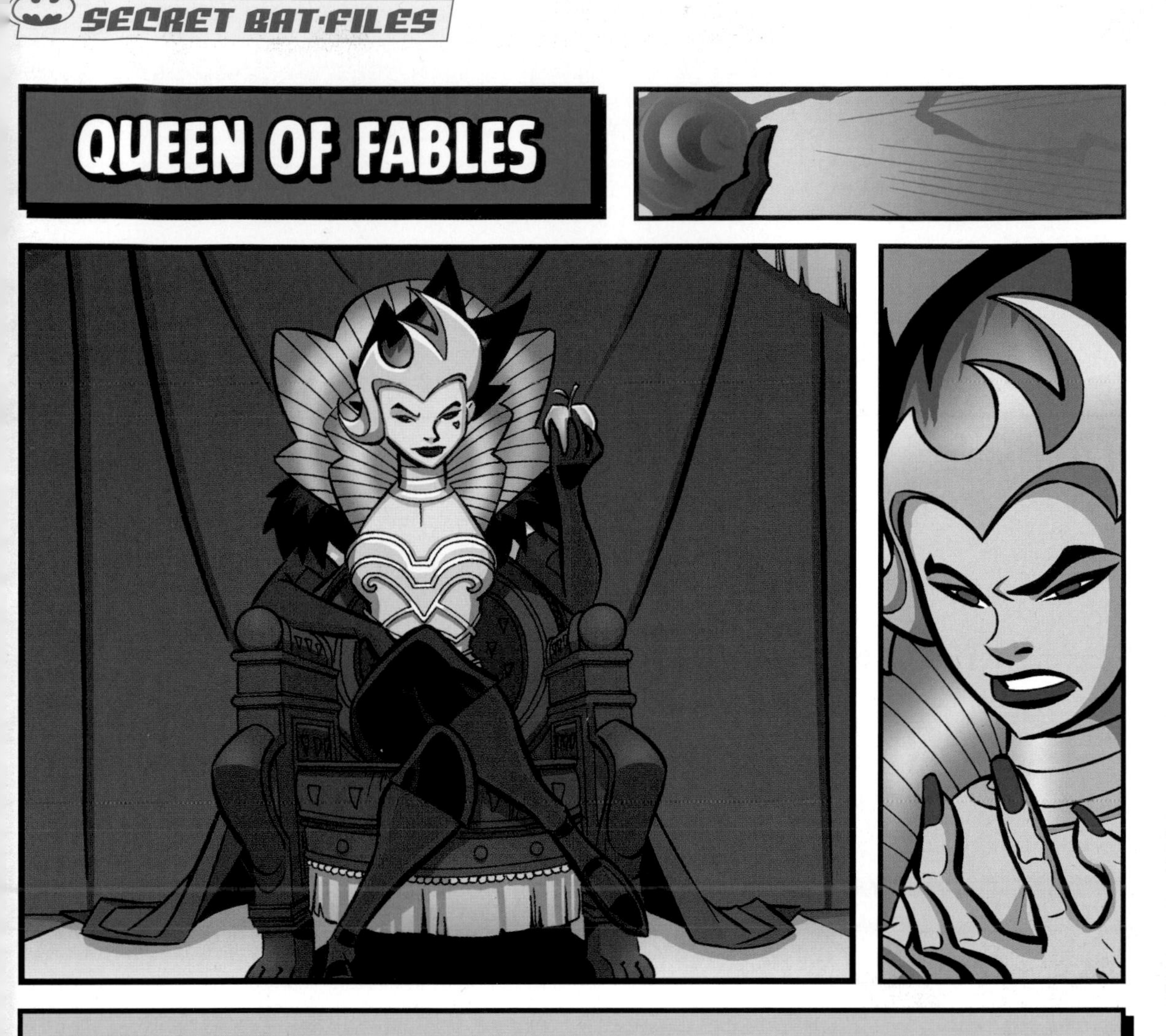

The Queen of Fables is an evil sorceress whose power comes from the darkest magic found in fairy tales and fables. She is as vain as she is villainous, and only wants to live happily ever after in a twisted world of her own diabolical design.

TOP SECRET:
She is perhaps better known for her performance as the wicked stepmother in the original production of "Snow White".

CAPTAIN MARVEL

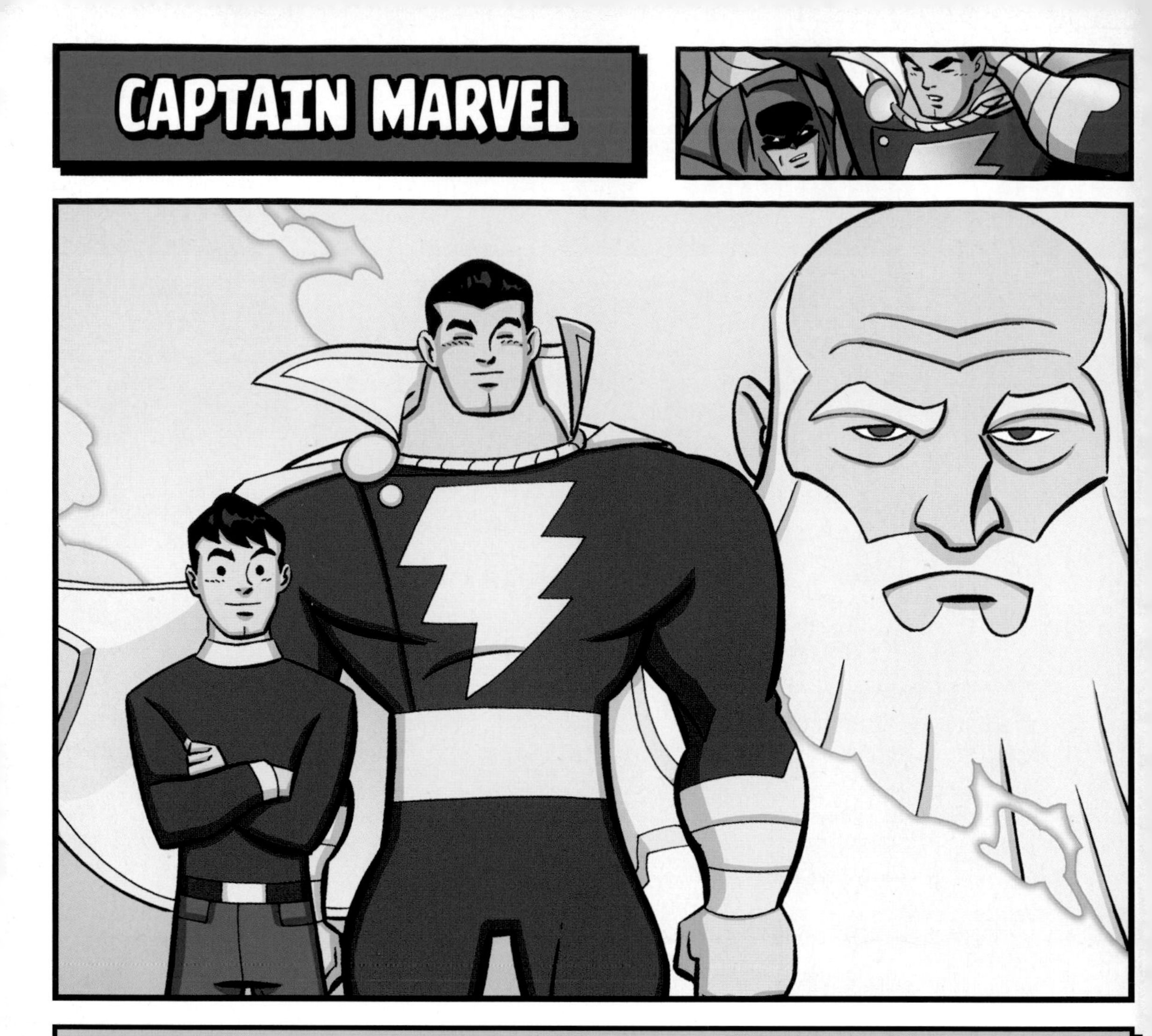

By invoking the name of the mighty wizard Shazam, Billy Batson, boy reporter for station *WHIZ*, is given the wisdom of Solomon, the strength of Hercules, the stamina of Atlas, the power of Zeus, the courage of Achilles, and the speed of Mercury to become Captain Marvel - the world's mightiest mortal.

TOP SECRET:
Captain Marvel's nickname is "The Big Red Cheese". But he's a good sport about it.

J. TORRES WRITER

J. Torres won the Shuster Award for Outstanding Writer for his work on *Batman: Legends of the Dark Knight*, *Love As a Foreign Language*, and *Teen Titans Go*. He is also the writer of the Eisner Award nominated *Alison Dare* and the YALSA listed *Days Like This* and *Lola: A Ghost Story*. Other comic book credits include *Avatar: The Last Airbender*, *Legion of Super-Heroes in the 31st Century*, *Ninja Scroll*, *Wonder Girl*, *Wonder Woman*, and *WALL-E: Recharge*.

CARLO BARBERI PENCILLER

Carlo Barberi is a professional comic book illustrator. He has worked for today's top publishers, such as DC Comics, Marvel, and Dark Horse. His credits include *Batman: The Brave and the Bold*, *Justice League Unlimited*, and *Deadpool*.

TERRY BEATTY INKER

Terry Beatty has been a professional comic book illustrator and inker for many years. His works for DC Comics include *The Batman Strikes!* and more.

baffled puzzled or confused

dilemma situation involving two or more difficult choices

enchanted magical

exclusive available only to certain people, or in a certain place

fable story that teaches a lesson, or an untrue story

sinister seeming evil and threatening

sorceress female wizard or magician

wicked very bad, cruel, or evil

VISUAL QUESTIONS & PROMPTS

1. Why do you think the Queen of Fables' mirror shows Shazam's name in this panel? Explain your answer using details from the story.

2. This illustration has lots of straight, purple lines moving away from Shazam. What purpose do the lines serve? Why do you think the artists chose to use them in this particular panel?

3. Why is there a red outline around the Queen of Fables' speech balloon? Why is Shazam's name bolded and in red in the second panel? Are they related? Explain.

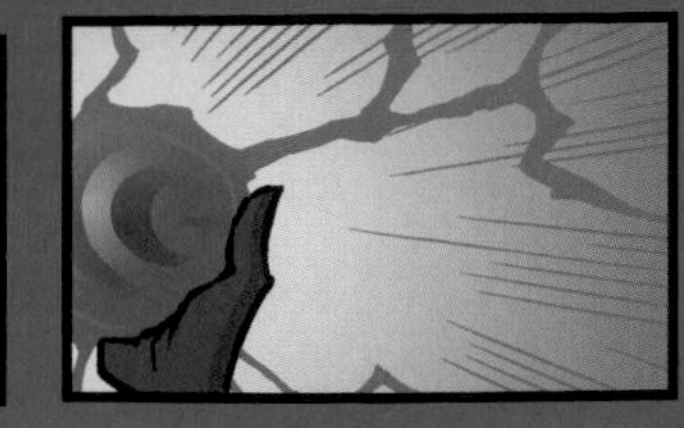

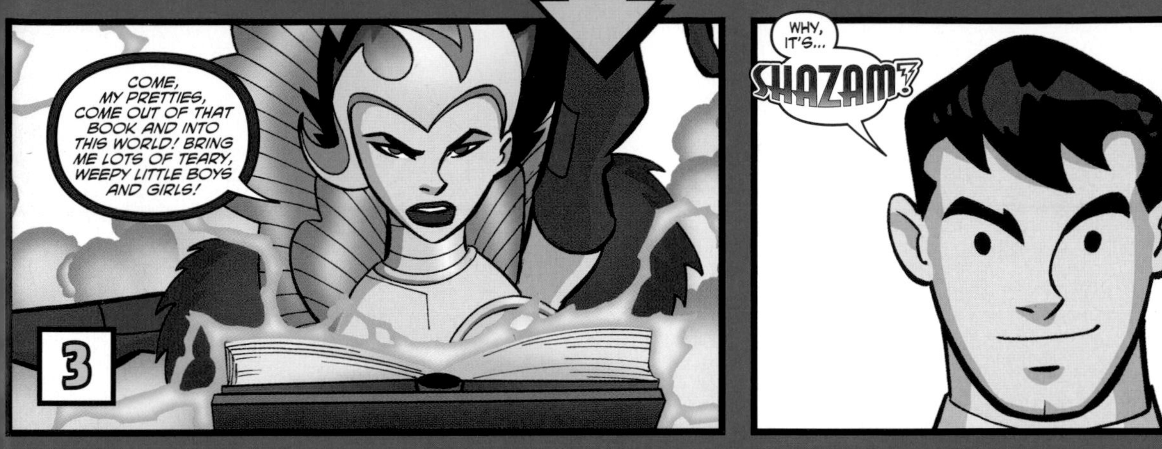

4. In the two panels below, parts of Shazam and Batman's bodies overlap the nearby panels. Why do you think the artists decided to show the heroes overlapping the panel borders?

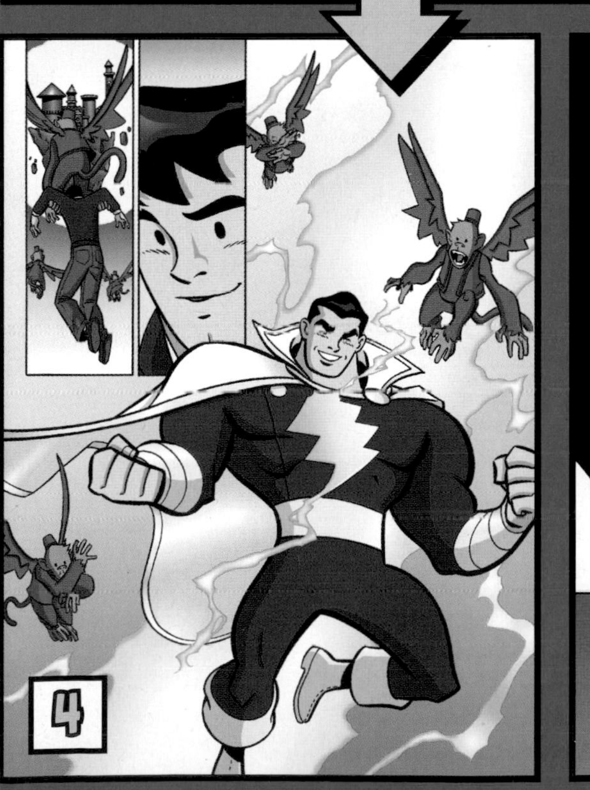

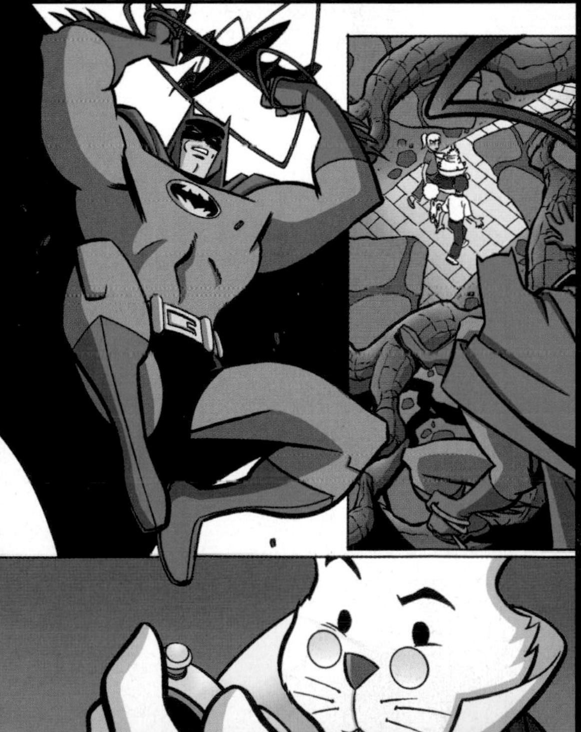

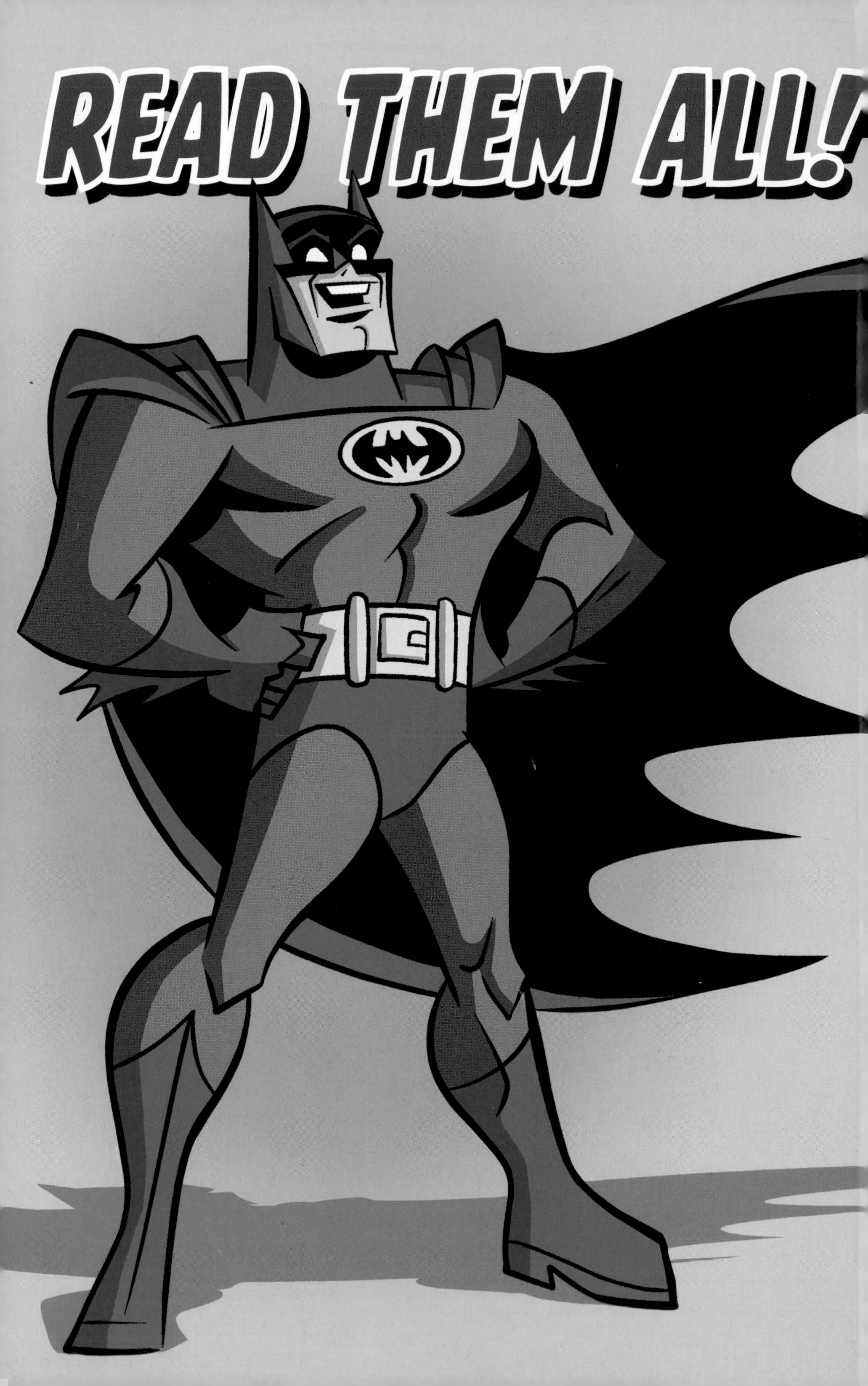
READ THEM ALL!

BATMAN
THE BRAVE AND THE BOLD®

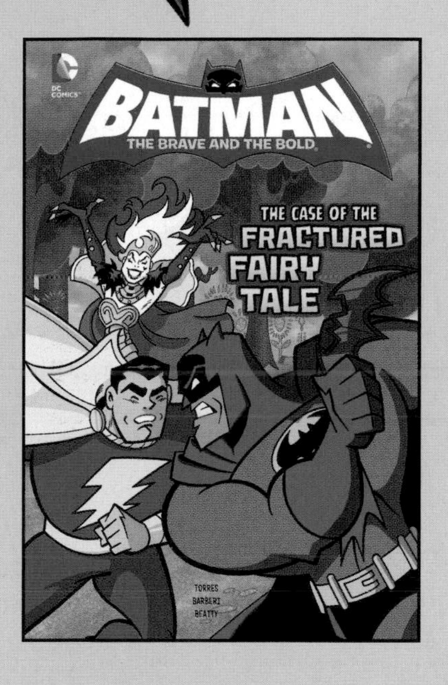

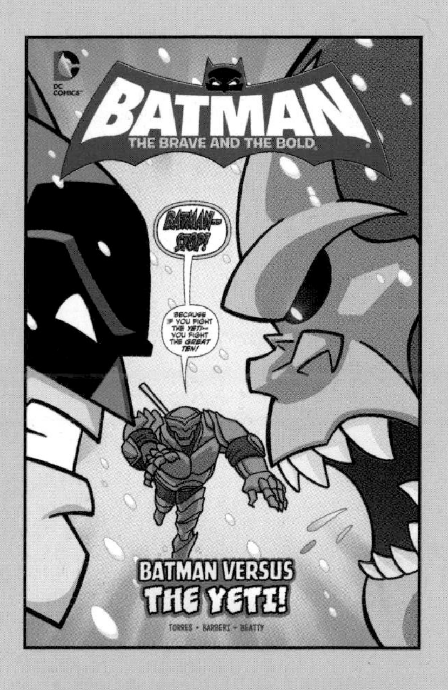

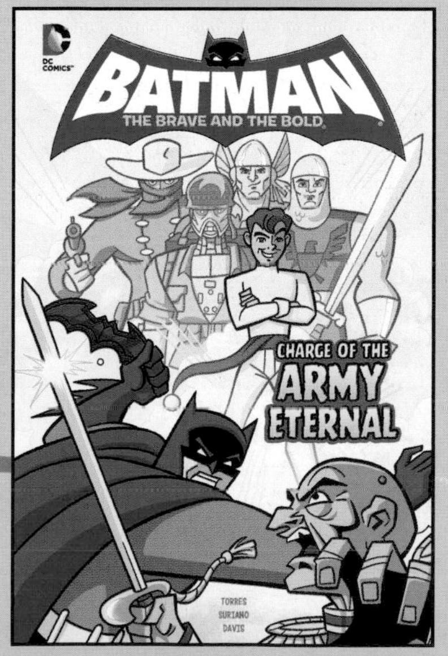

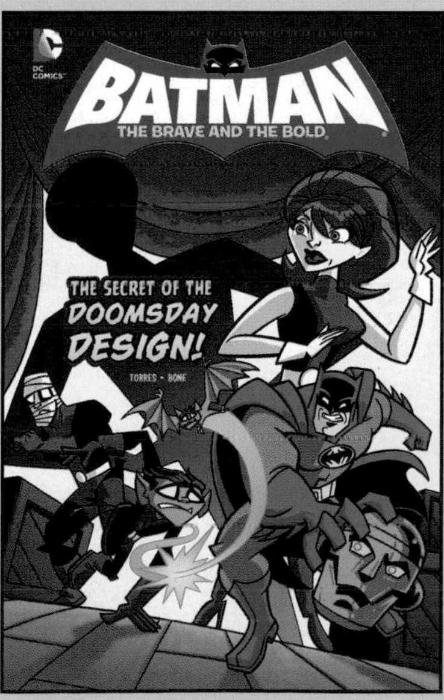